Have You Met My Other Half?

THE ORIGIN OF CLICHÉS - A CARTOONIST'S VIEW
ANTHONY GRANT

 Robson Books

First published in Great Britain in 1990 by Robson Books Ltd,
Bolsover House, 5-6 Clipstone Street, London W1P 7EB

British Library Cataloguing in Publication Data
Grant, Anthony *1958–*
The origins of the cliché.
  1. English humorous cartoons
  1. Title
  741.5942

ISBN 0 86051 693 9

Printed in Great Britain by St Edmundsbury Press, Bury St Edmunds,
Suffolk.

Foreword
by Maureen Lipman

Anthony Grant is the man who has photographed me for my last (and only) three book jackets.

Nevertheless, I agreed to have a look at his book of cartoons. No, honestly, my heart was in my mouth (nice cartoon in that one, Anthony) for fear I wouldn't like what I saw, and would be too scared to say so in case my fourth book jacket made me look like Norman Tebbit.

Fortunately, thrillingly, this book made me BARK with laughter, and if you've a mind for a pun and a love of the clichéd phrase refreshingly rethought, then you may BARK too when you read it. But not too loudly or he'll give up the day job and I'll have to be photographed by Koo, or Bailey, or Newton or one of those other guys with their own Brownie Automatics.

Hand on heart, this book comes with my strongest recommendation. It's seriously funny.

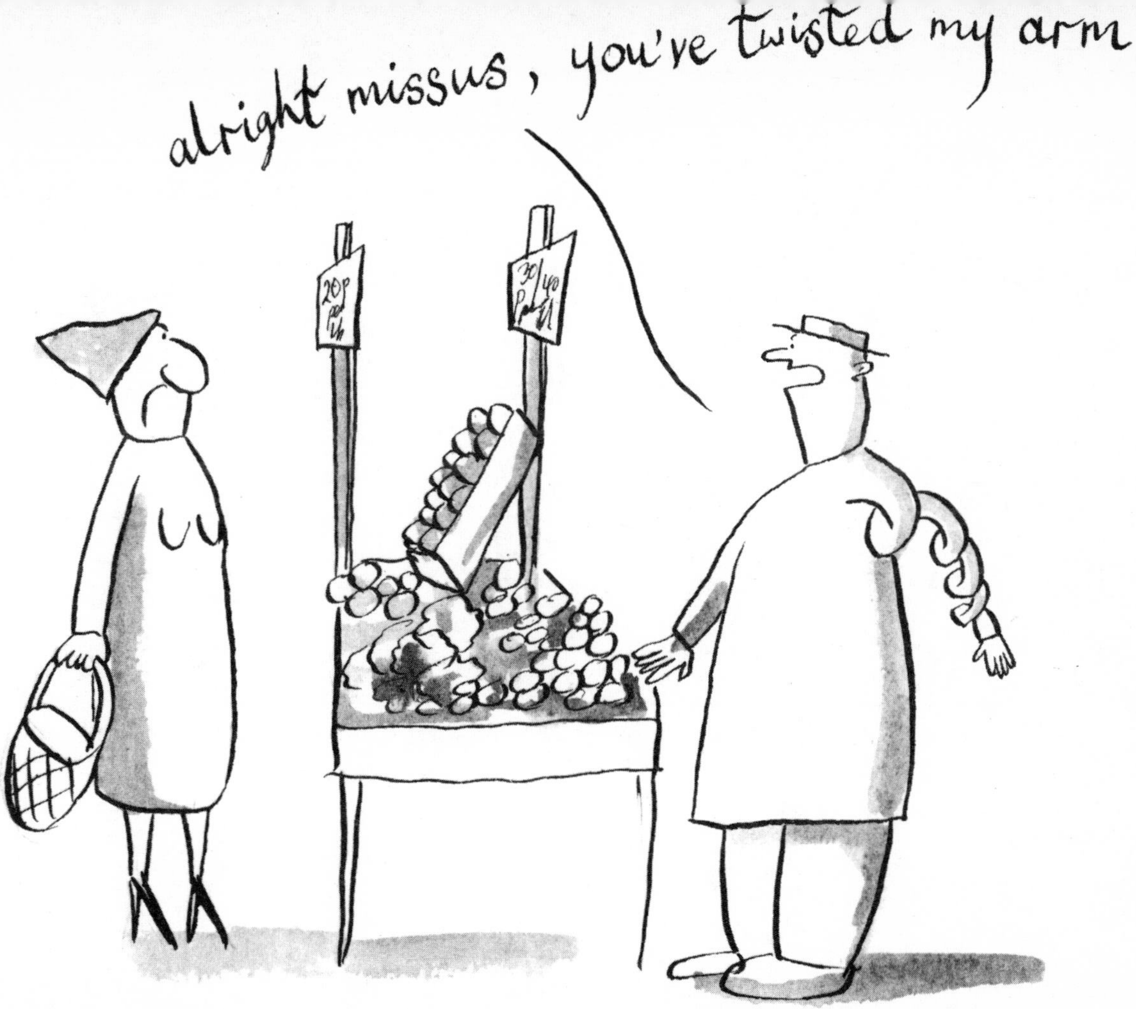
alright missus, you've twisted my arm

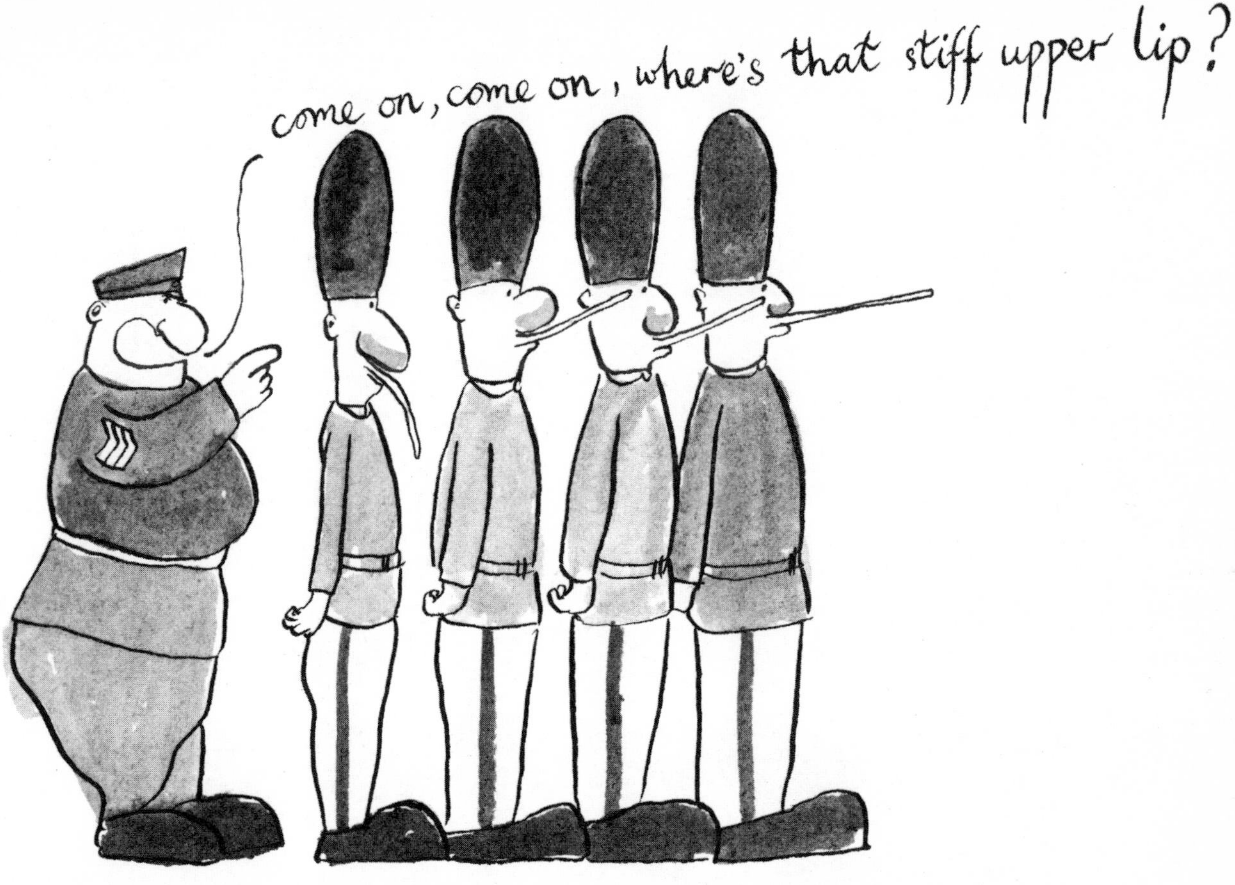
come on, come on, where's that stiff upper lip?

sit down my dear and take the weight off your feet

trust Hortensia to invite the world and his wife

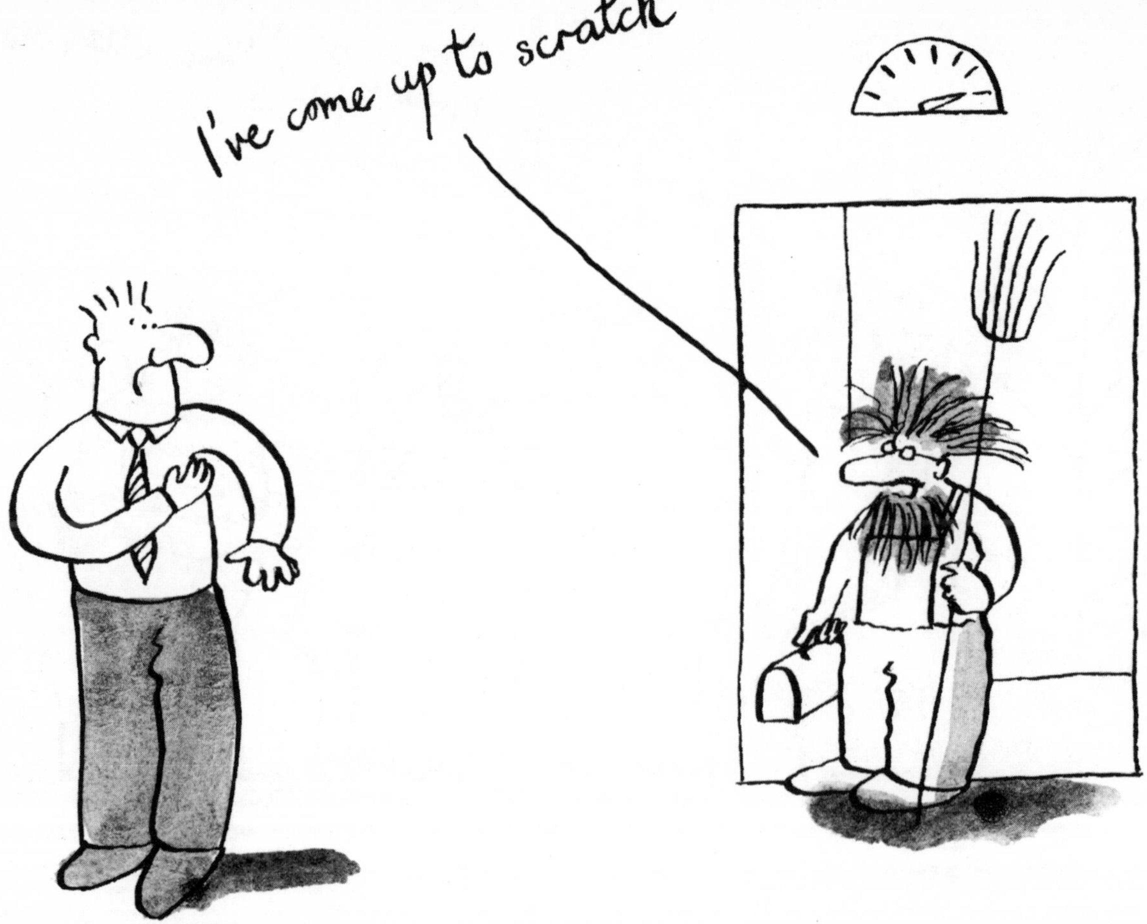
I've come up to scratch

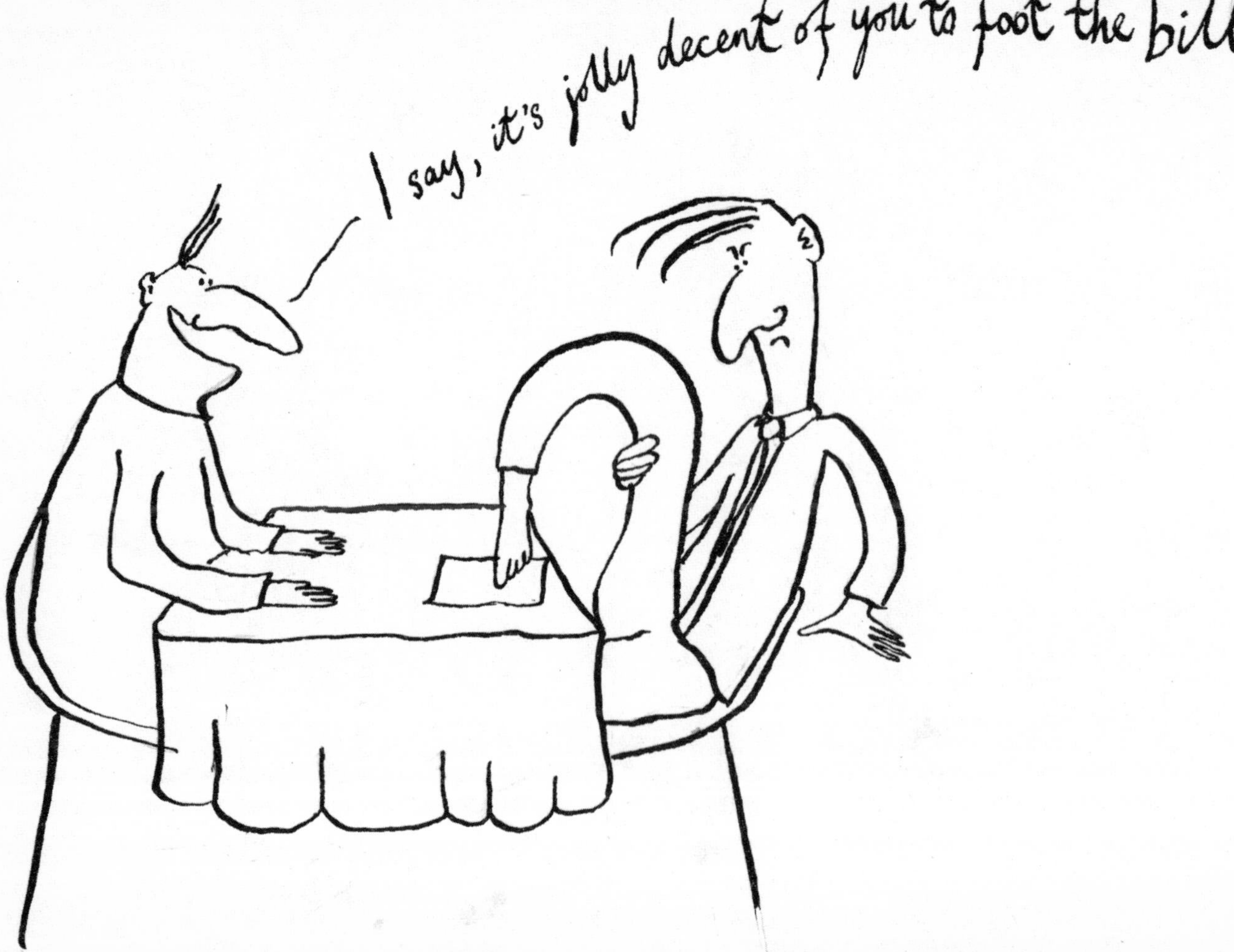
I say, it's jolly decent of you to foot the bill

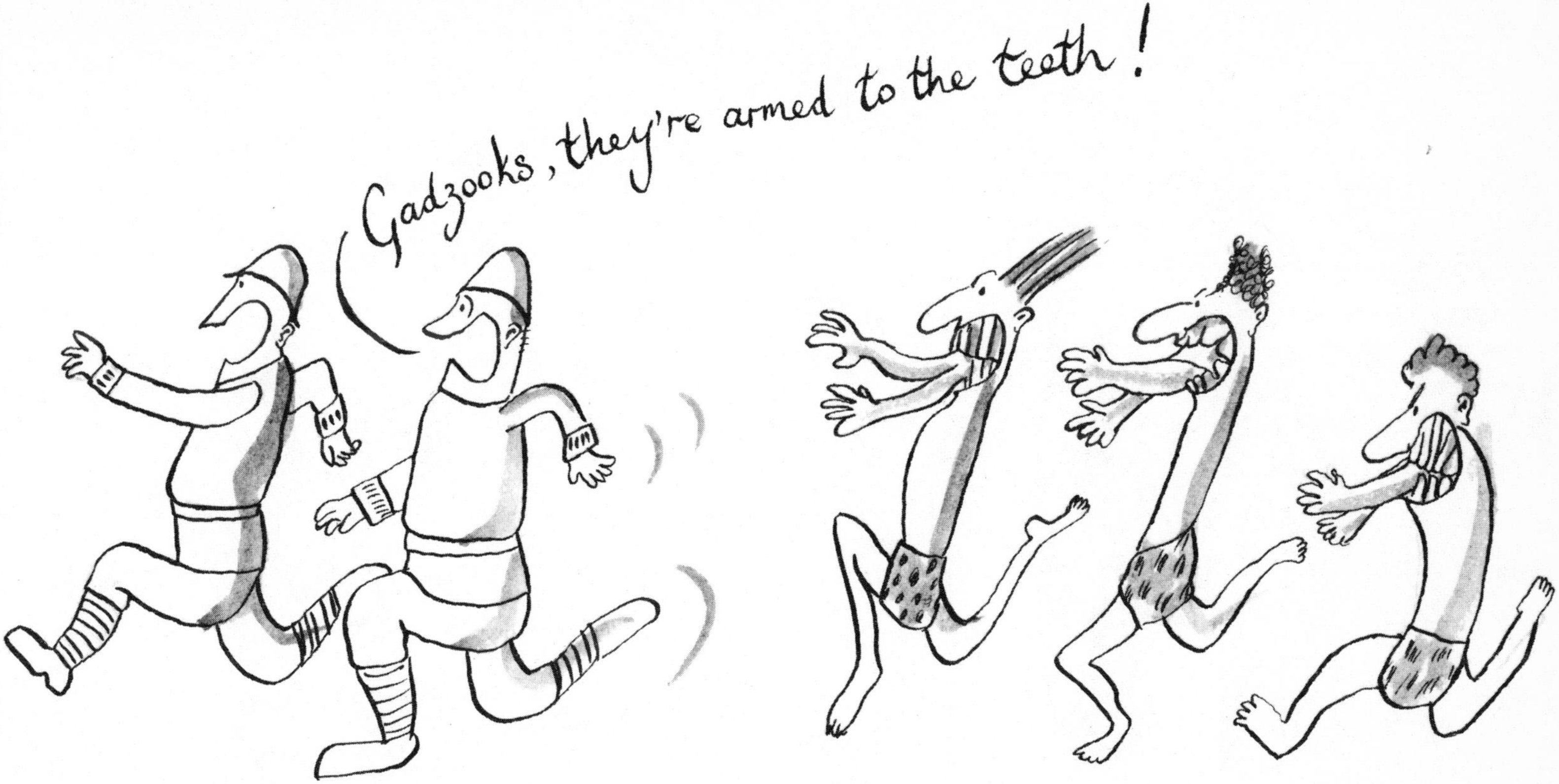
Gadzooks, they're armed to the teeth!

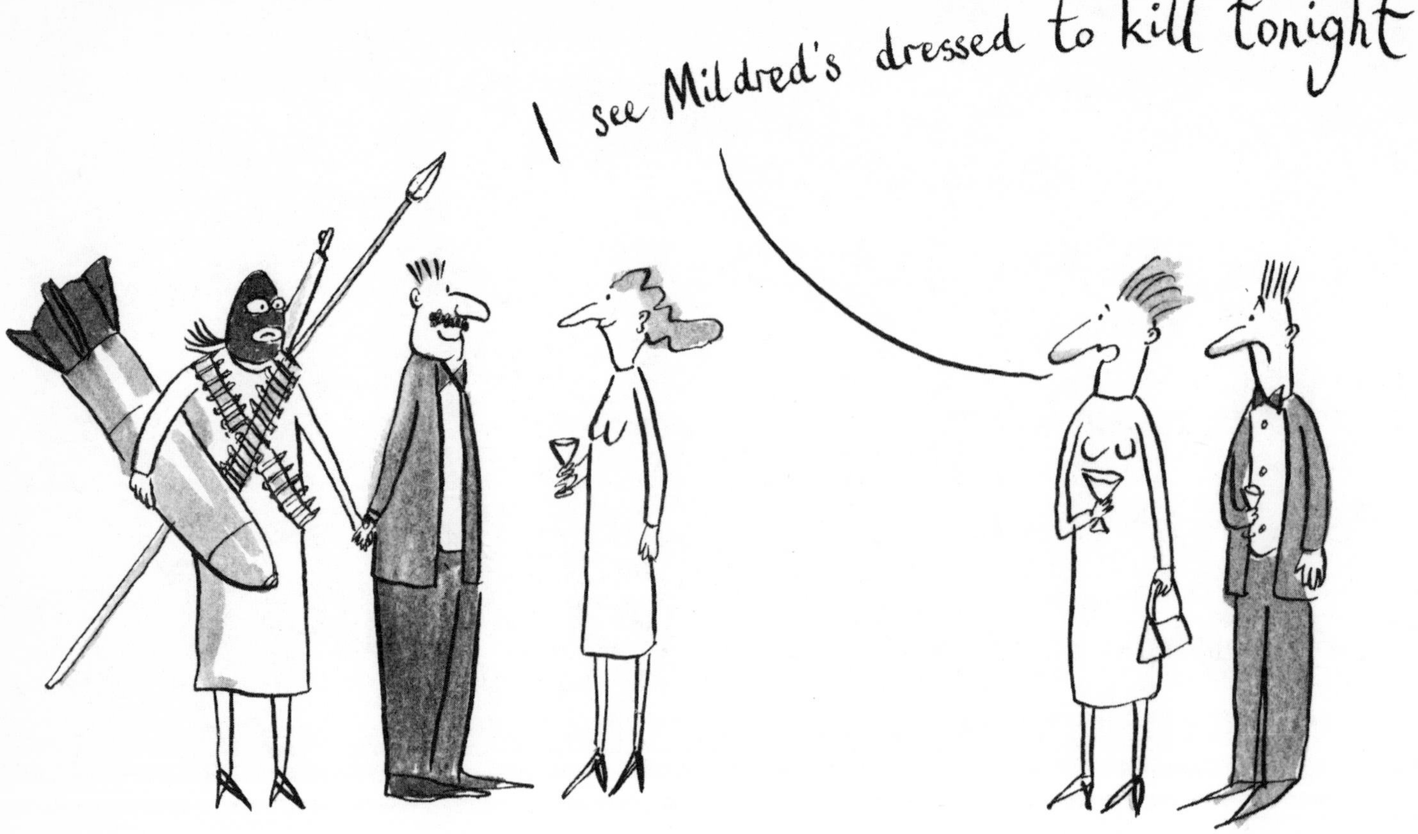
I see Mildred's dressed to kill tonight

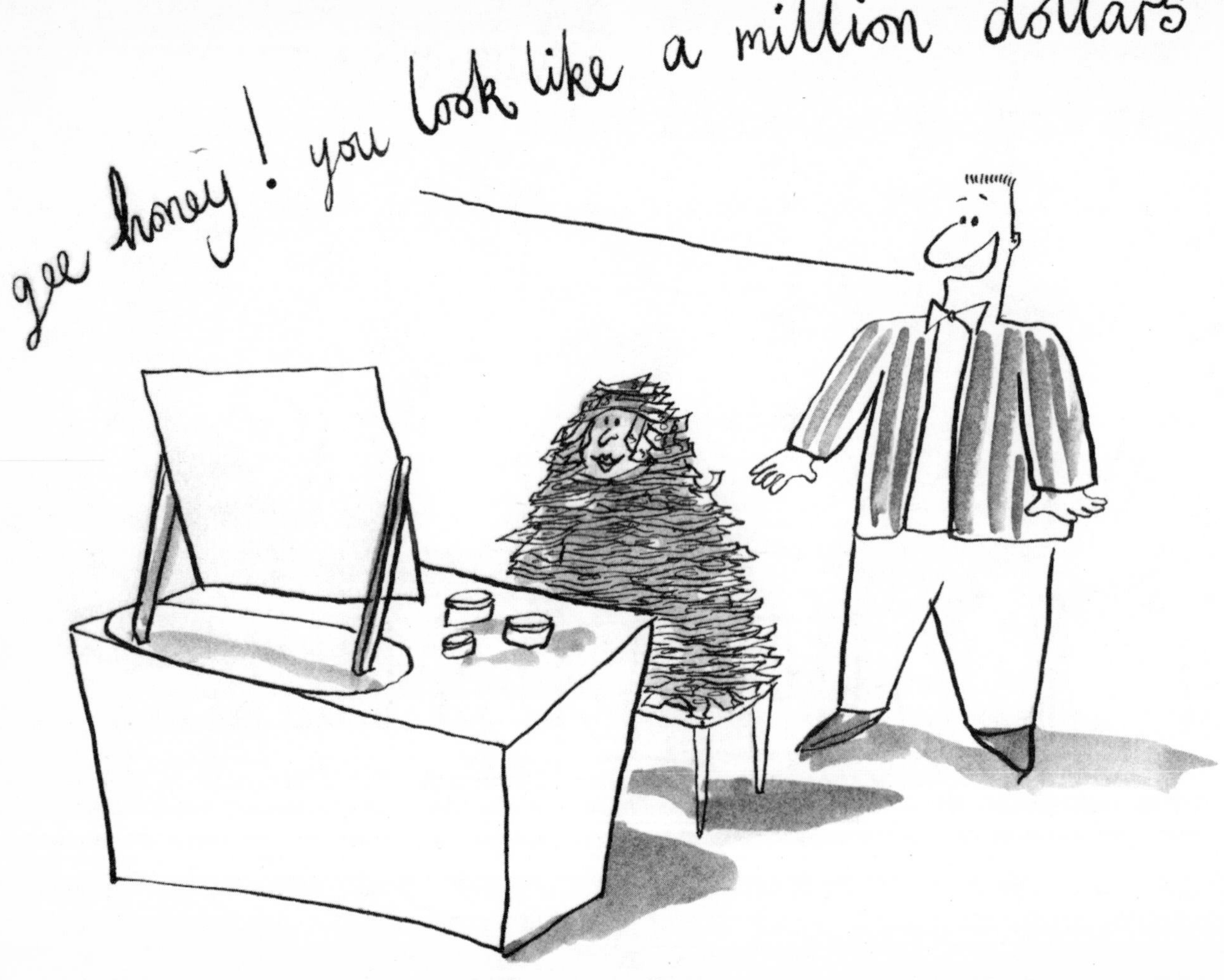
gee honey! you look like a million dollars

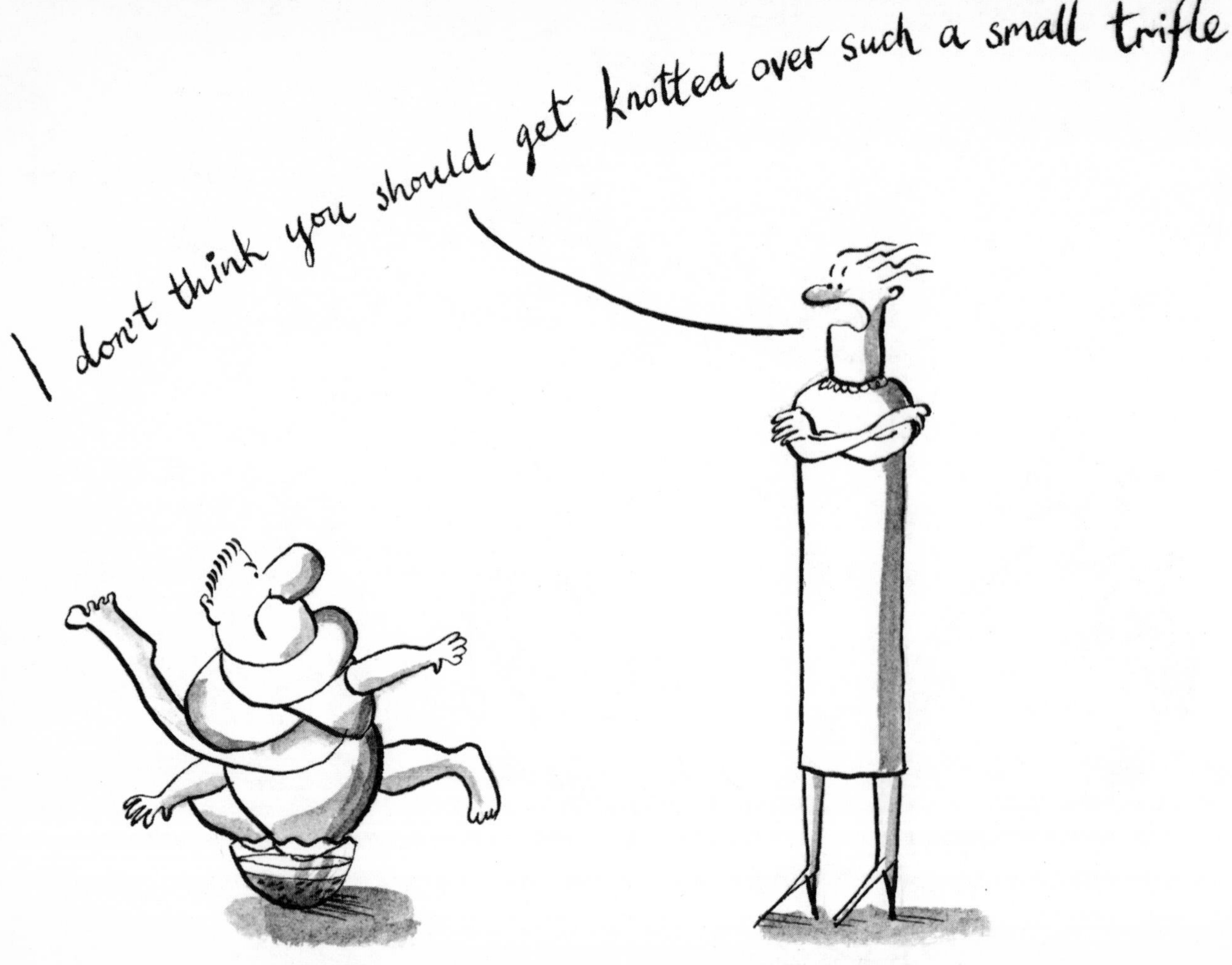
I don't think you should get knotted over such a small trifle

Seamus you old devil

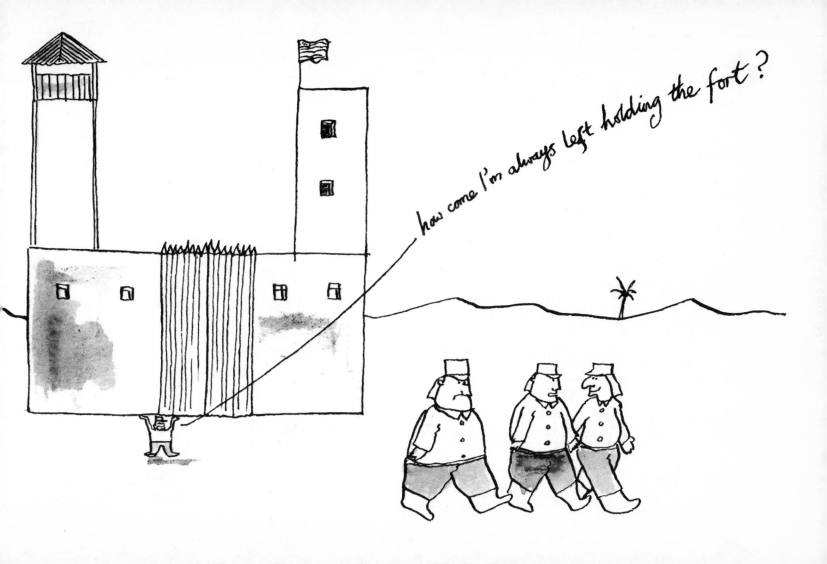

Just between you, me and the gatepost ...

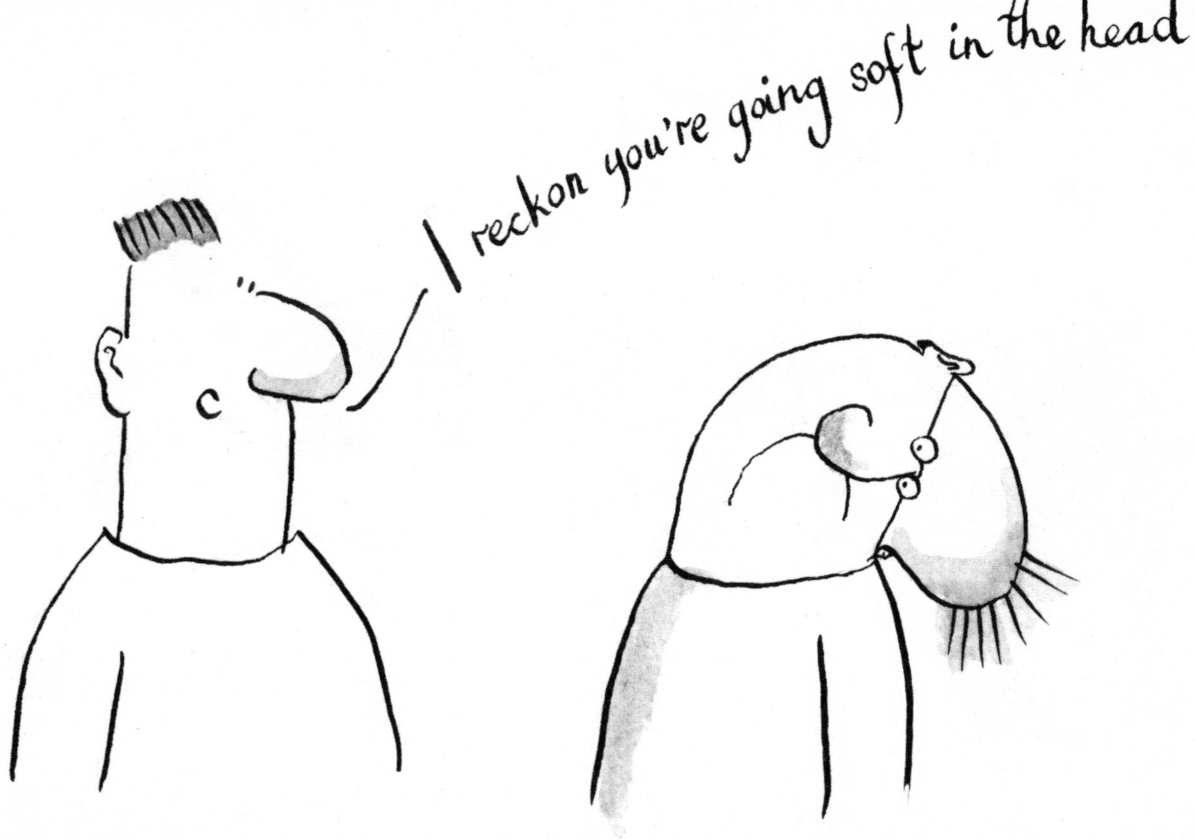
I reckon you're going soft in the head

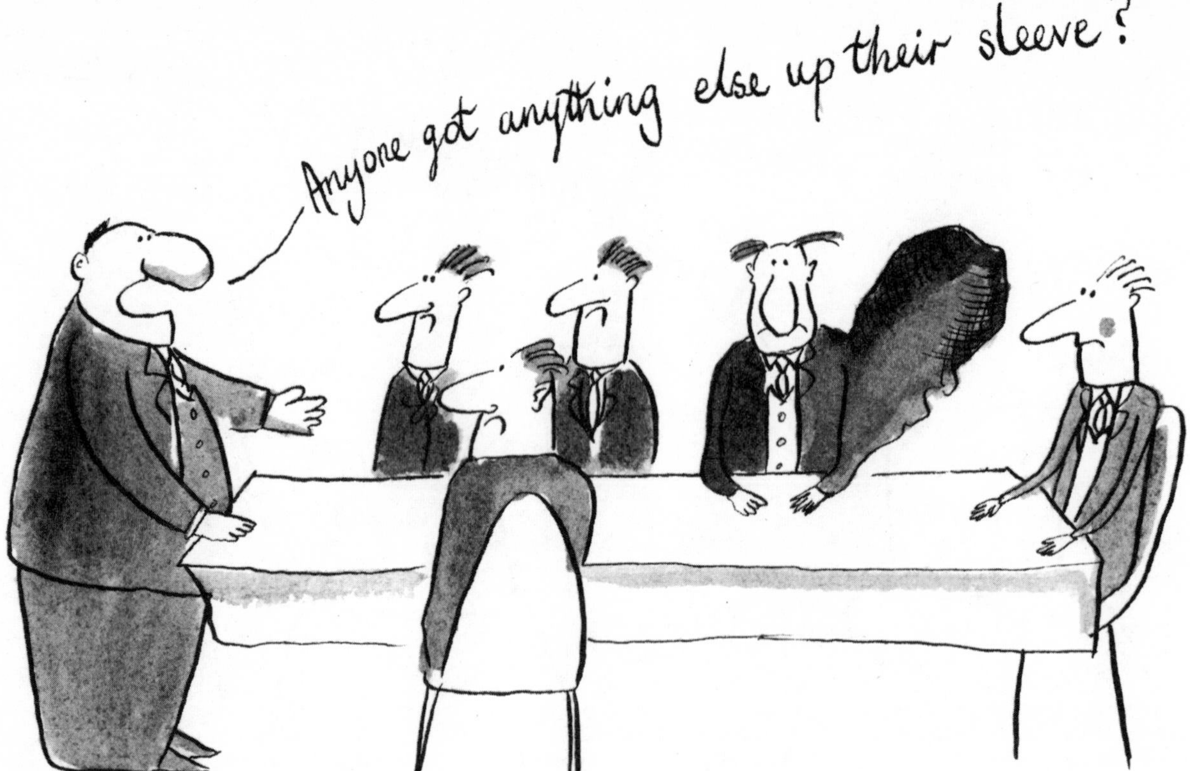
Anyone got anything else up their sleeve?

what's the matter Deidre? You've been a bag of nerves all evening

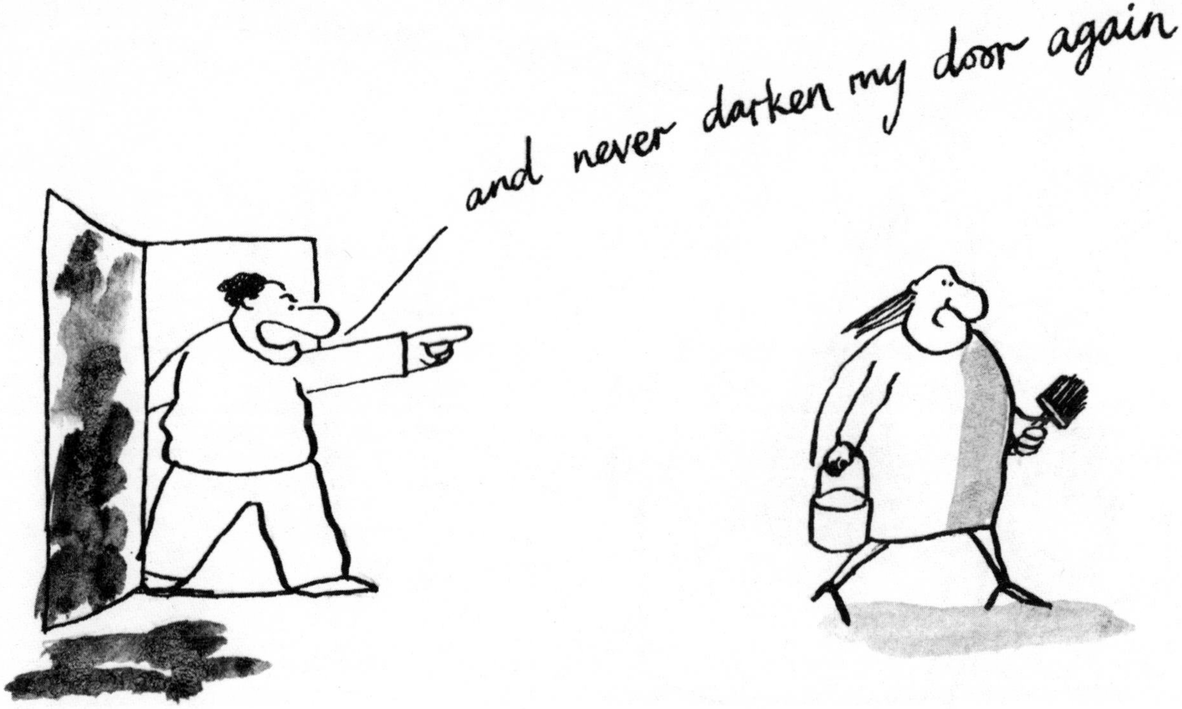
and never darken my door again

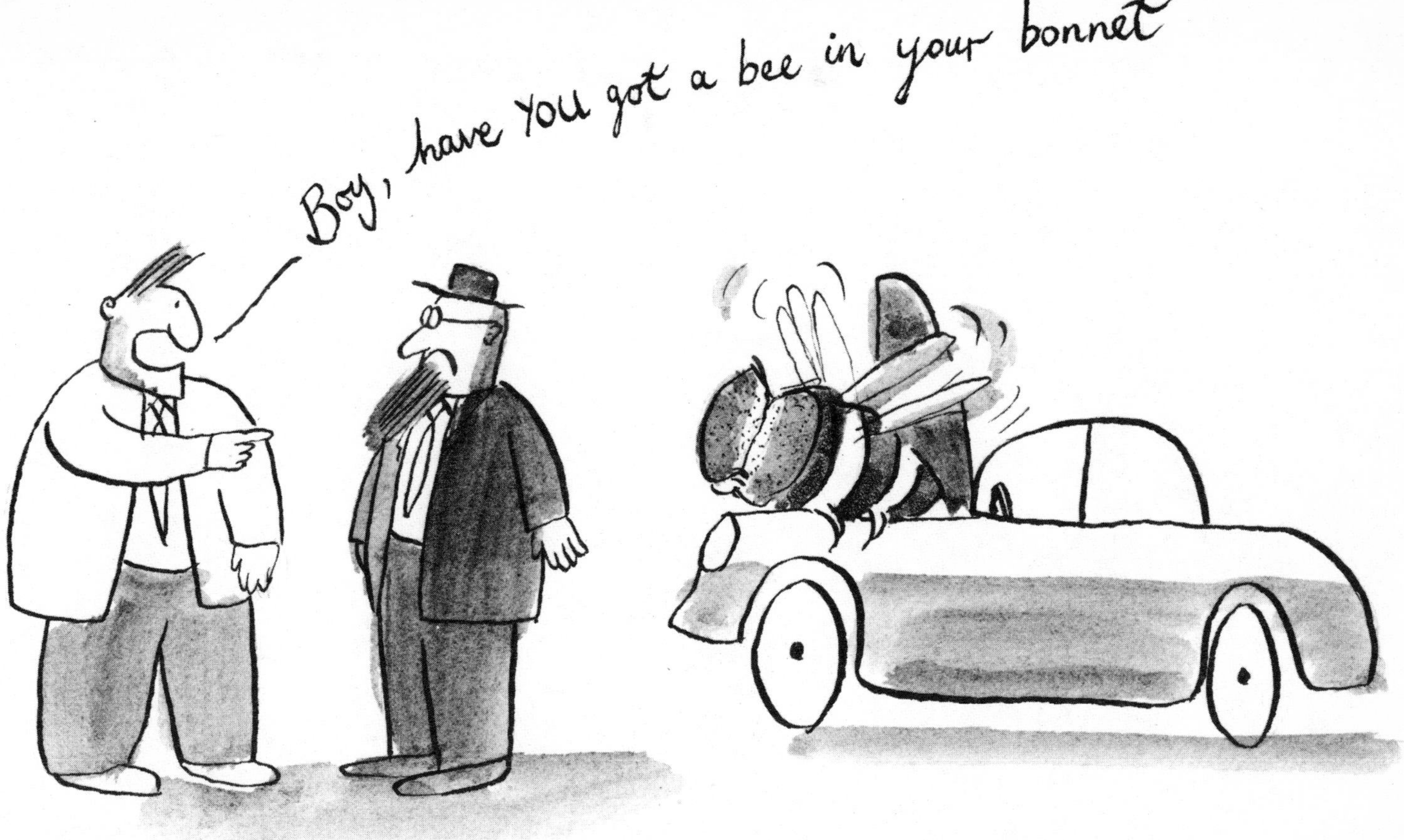
Boy, have YOU got a bee in your bonnet

and it won't do any good stewing in your own juice

Al Fresco and Bête Noire!

that's it lad, keep thy nose t' grindstone

I do wish you wouldn't rack your brains over those crosswords

he tends to speak volumes

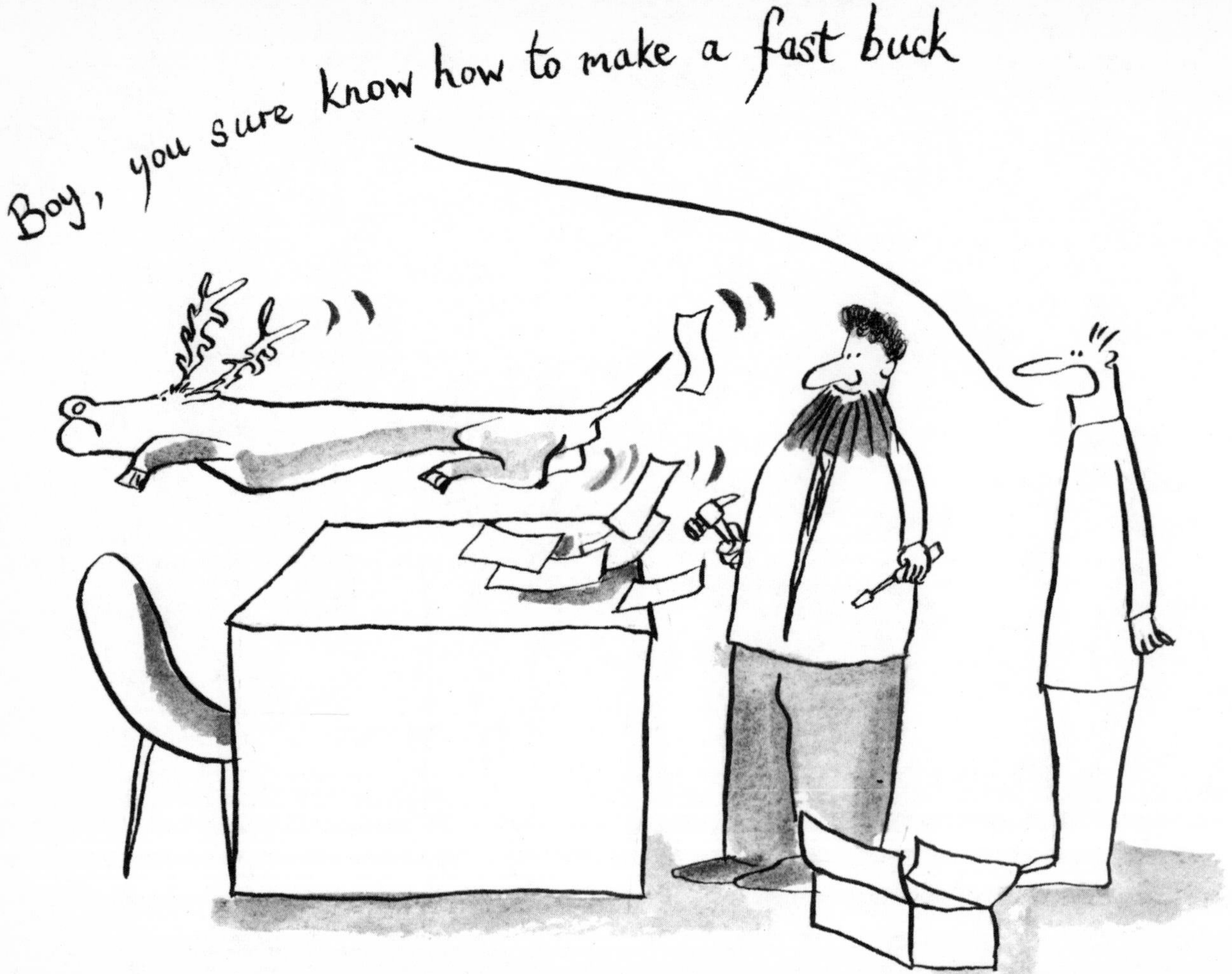
Boy, you sure know how to make a fast buck

he's every inch a ruler

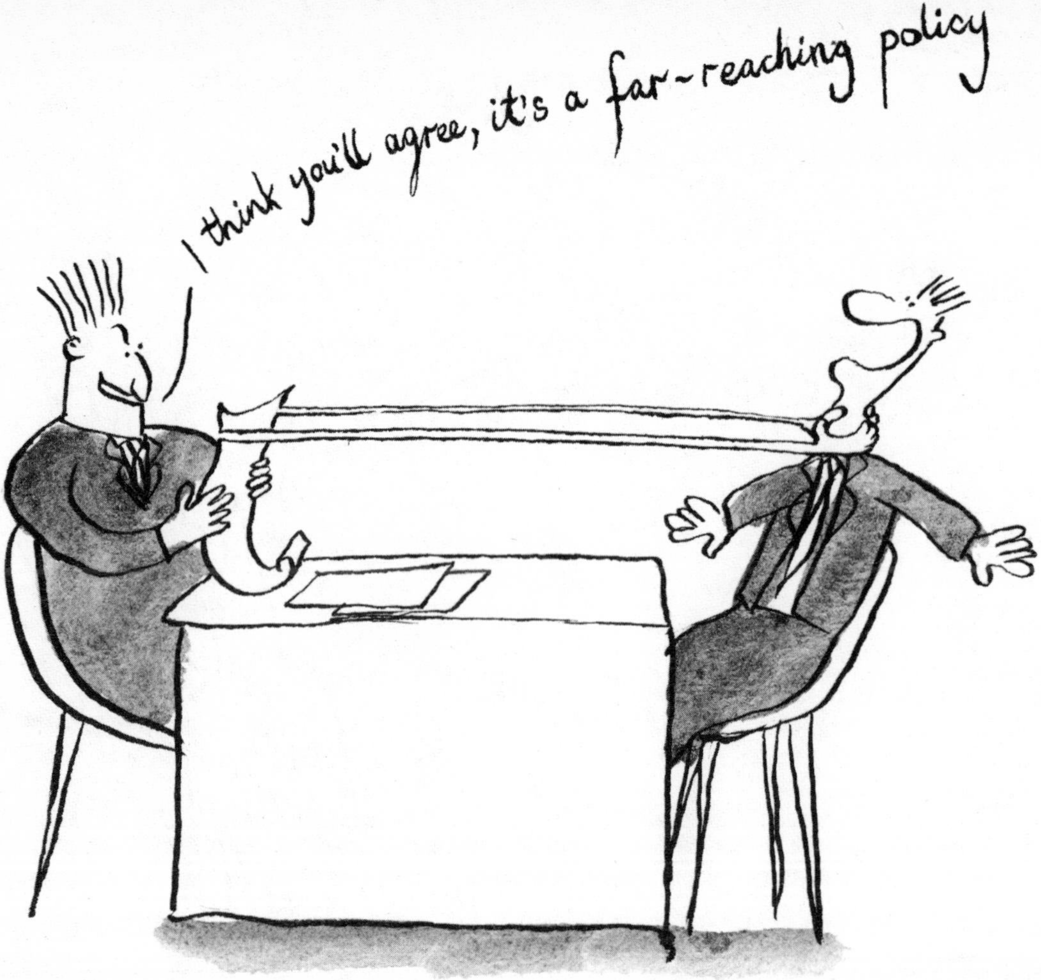
I think you'll agree, it's a far-reaching policy

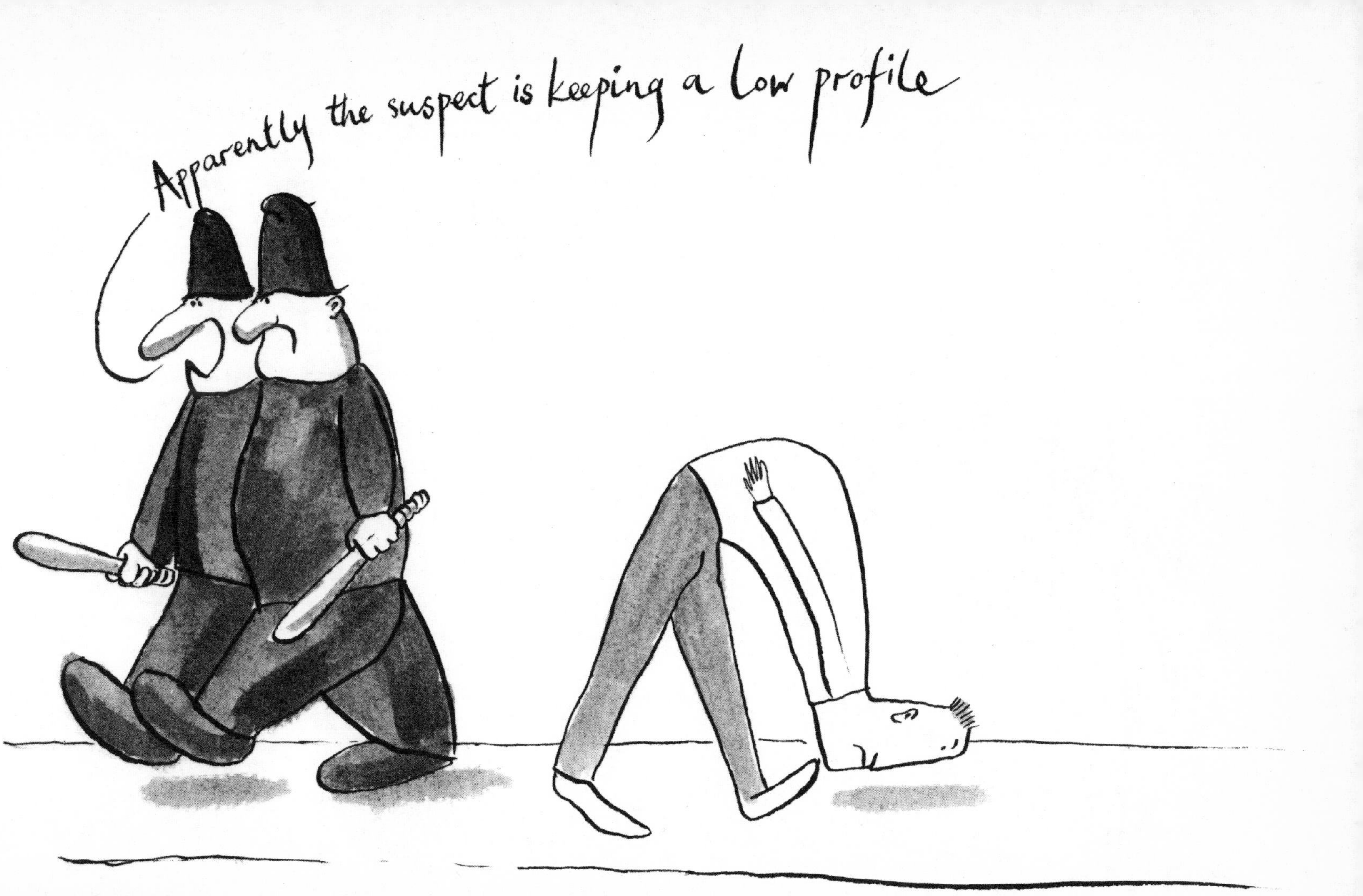
Apparently the suspect is keeping a low profile

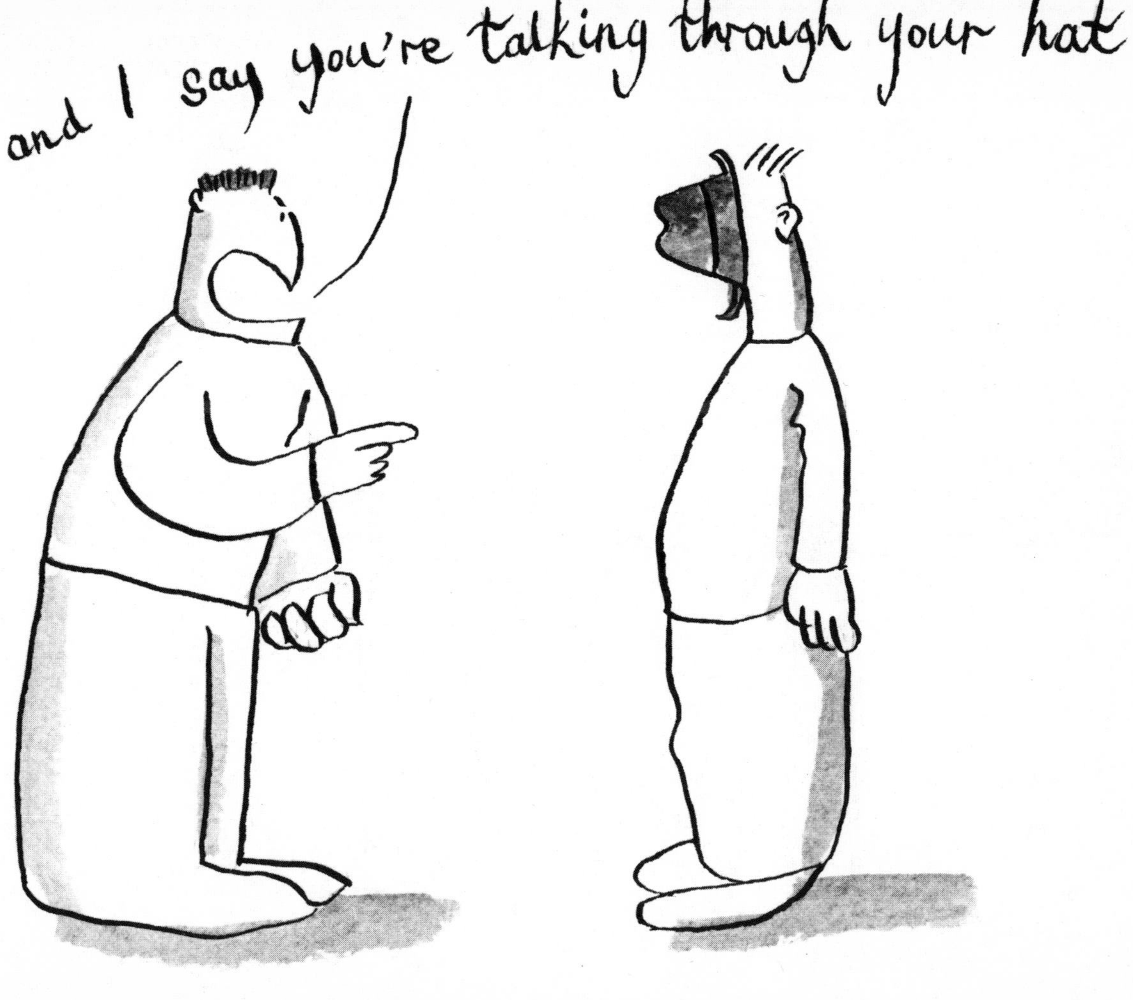
and I say you're talking through your hat

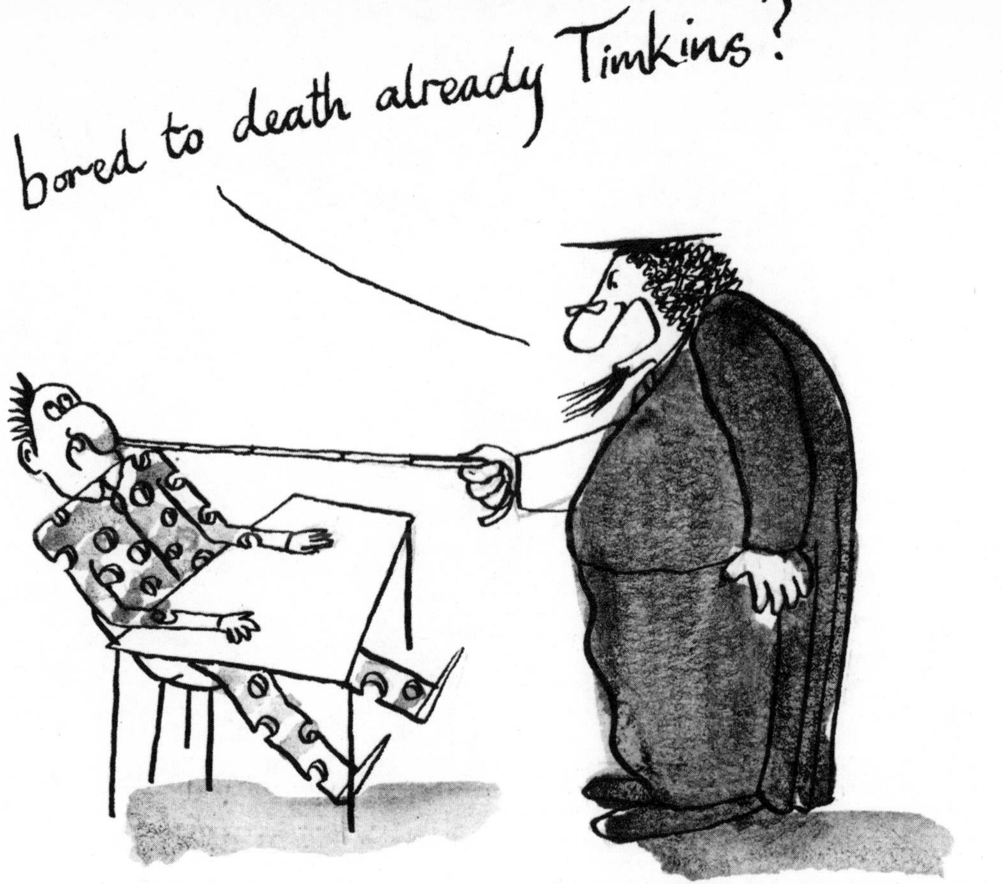
bored to death already Timkins?

Take a break Smithson, you're getting too absorbed in your work

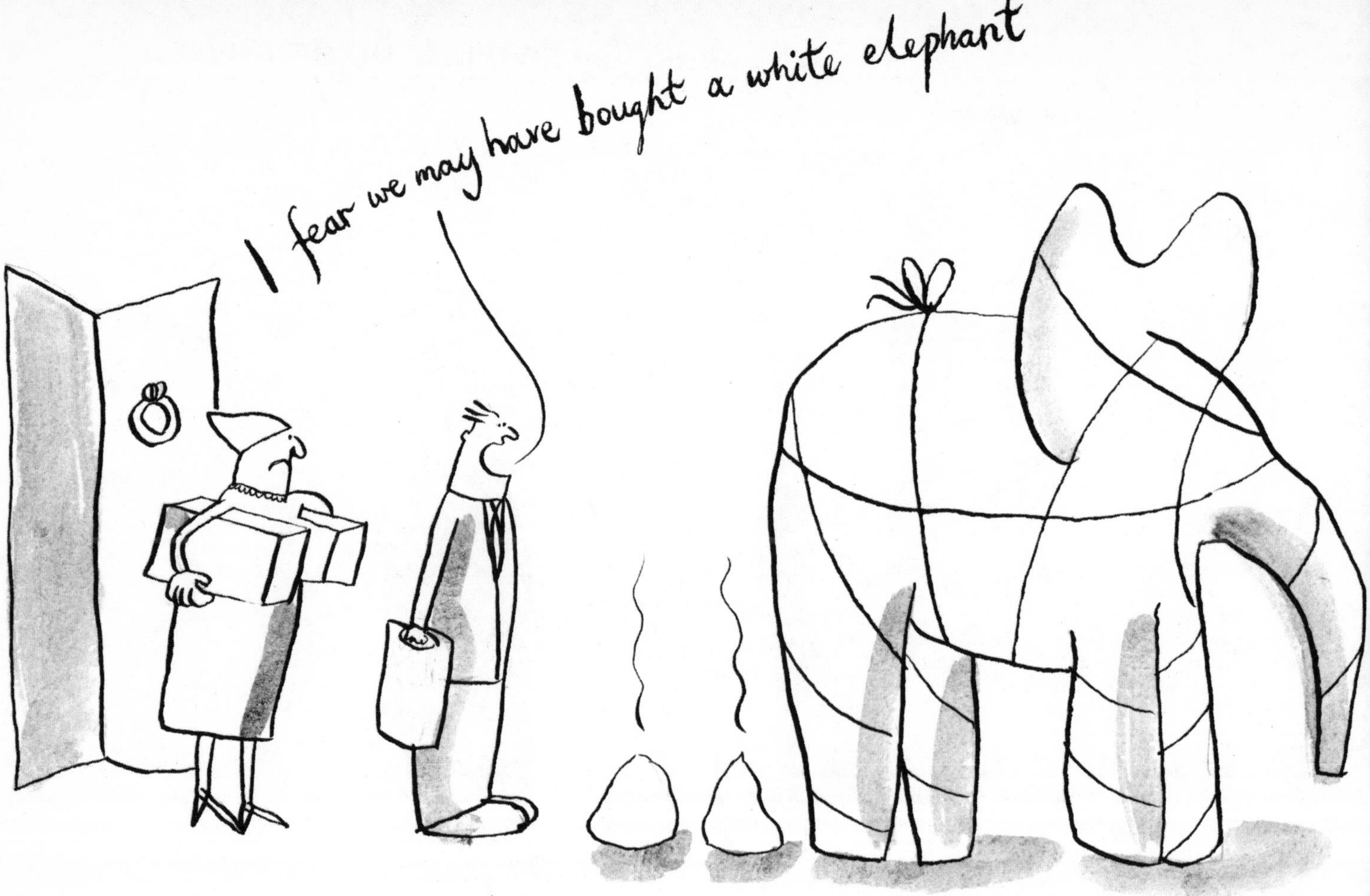
I fear we may have bought a white elephant

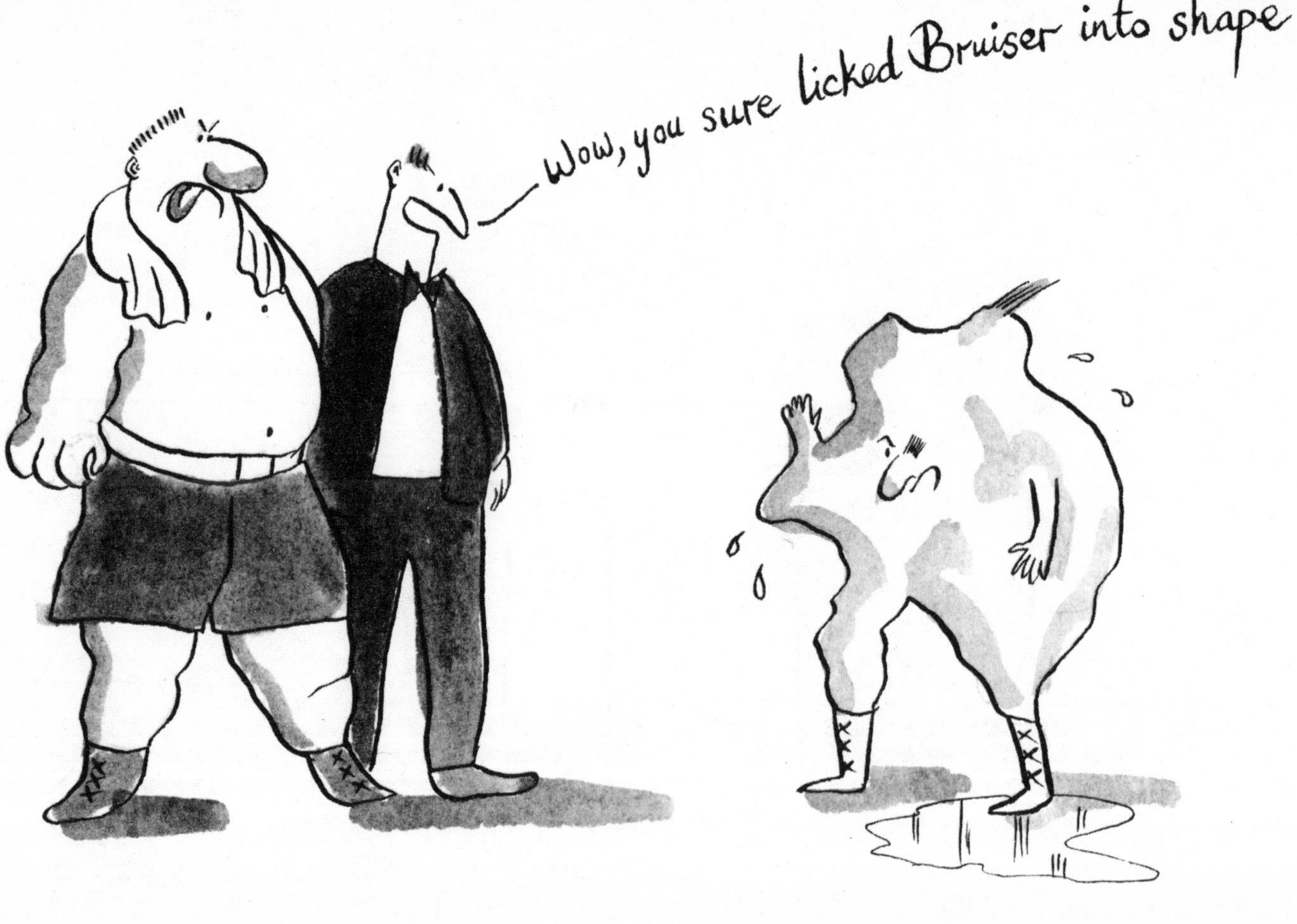
Wow, you sure licked Bruiser into shape

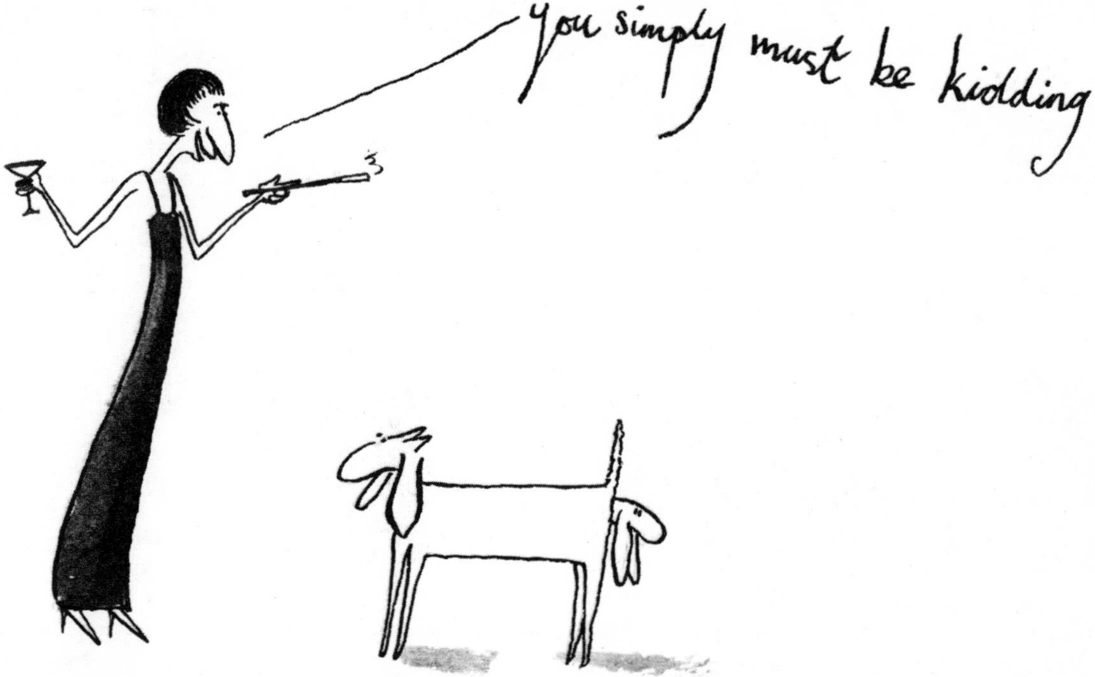
You simply must be kidding

It's curtains for you Mulligan

... and remember, from now on we're keeping tabs on you Finlay

There, you can always trust Mummy to make you a square meal

this is no time to rest on your laurels boy

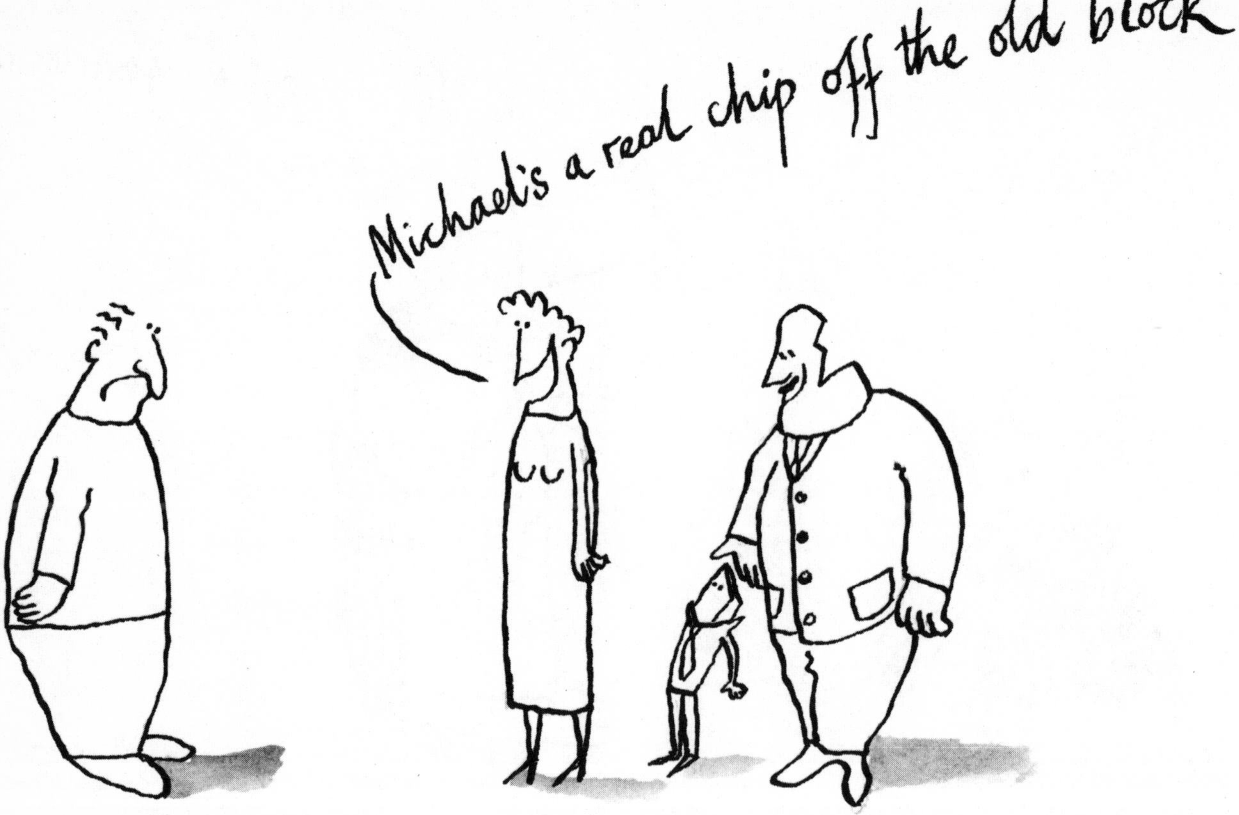
Michael's a real chip off the old block

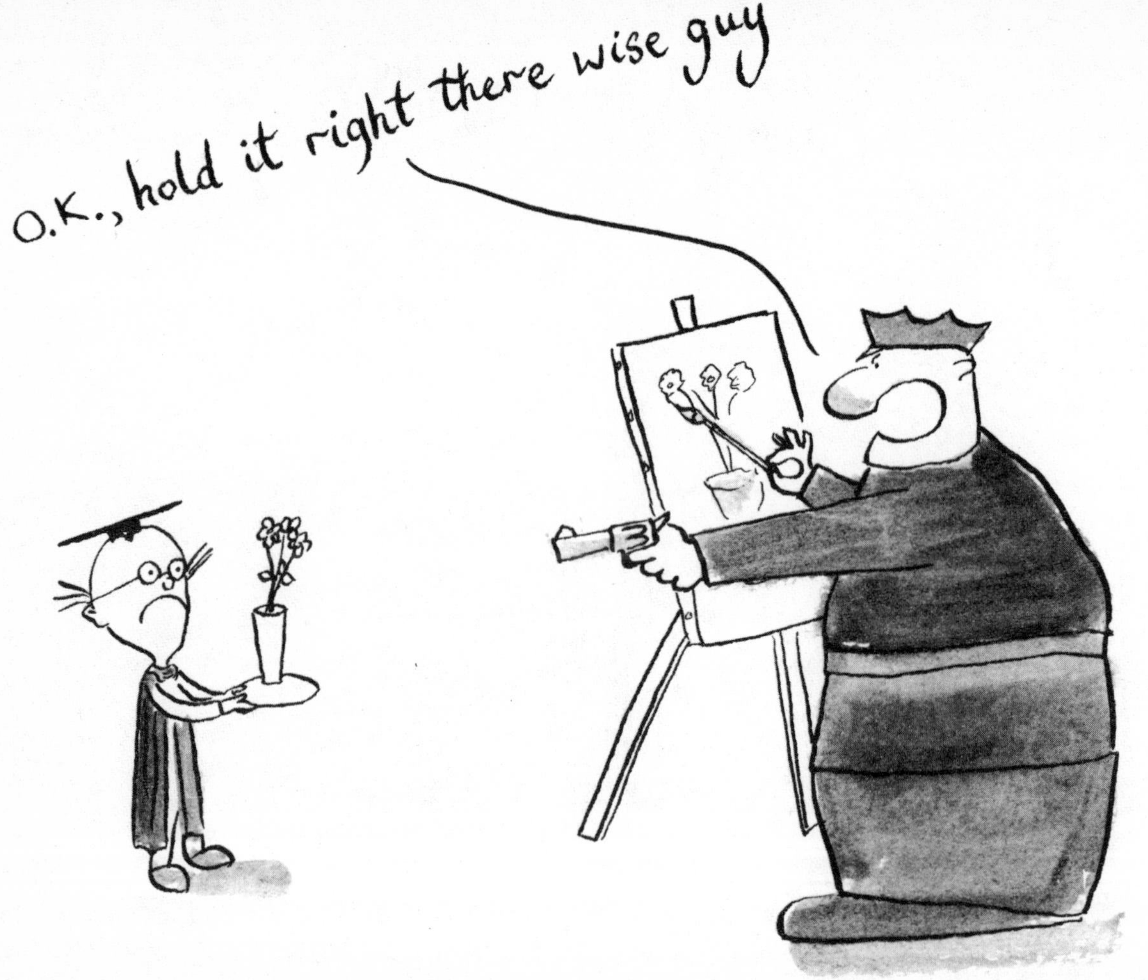
O.K., hold it right there wise guy